Holocaus
and Smite the Heathens,
Charlie Brown

Shalom Auslander

Holocaust Tips for Kids and Smite the Heathens, Charlie Brown

PICADOR SHOTS

First published 2006 by Picador
an imprint of Pan Macmillan Ltd
Pan Macmillan, 20 New Wharf Road, London N1 9RR
Basingstoke and Oxford
Associated companies throughout the world
www.panmacmillan.com

ISBN-13: 978-0-330-44572-6
ISBN-10: 0-330-44572-3

1 3 5 7 9 8 6 4 2

A CIP catalogue record for this book is available from
the British Library.

Typeset by Intype Libra Ltd
Printed and bound in Great Britain by
Mackays of Chatham plc, Chatham, Kent

Holocaust Tips for Kids

[Parents: Next Tuesday we will be commemorating Holocaust Remembrance Day with an all-day program of films and lectures for students in grades 4–8, much of which will be graphic and potentially disturbing. Please sign and return this permission slip so that your child may attend. Thank you.]

If the Nazis come in the middle of the night and try to take me away to a concentration camp, these are the things I plan to take with me: some food, my allowance money, a sleeping bag, my Walkman, a toothbrush, a knife from the kitchen, my nunchucks, some Ninja throwing stars, a flashlight and my comic books.

Holocaust means "burned up."

Kristallnacht means "The Night of Broken Glass."

On November 10, 1938, the Nazis broke the Jews' store windows and burned down the shuls. That's why it's called "The Night of Broken Glass."

If ever there's a Night of Broken Glass where you live, leave.

In the movie *Holocaust,* the Weisses waited too long after Kristallnacht to leave. Then they all died, except for their son Rudy. Their other son Karl was sent to Buchenwald.

Buchenwald was one of the largest concentration camps in Germany. It was opened in 1937.

"If you are at lunch, or if you have no appetite

4

*ear what the Germans have done, now is a
d time to switch off the radio, for I propose to
you of Buchenwald."*
—CBS news, seven years later, in 1945

he character of Karl Weiss was played by
es Woods, who also played one of the Israeli
Force pilots in the movie *Raid on Entebbe*. In
movie his name was Captain Sammy Berg.

ohn Saxon was also a pilot in *Raid on Entebbe*.
has a Black Belt in karate. He was in *Enter the
gon*.

'll leave right after the next Kristallnacht, and
ake Deena with me. Her parents won't want
to leave, but if we want to live, we'll have to go
away. There will be no time to waste. We can
к to the highway and hitchhike from there. It's
that far. Maybe Kevin's mom will give us a ride.

Ve'll probably go to Florida and stay in the
tainebleau Hotel in Miami. Deena goes there

every January with her family. They have a te
court and a pool.

Florida is 1,330 miles from New York.
need to get to a highway called I–95 South. Fi
there it's a straight drive all the way to Miam

Kevin isn't Jewish. In the summer, we ride b
cles together. My mother says his mother is a
good anti-Semite.

*In 1934, The New York Times described
news that Nazis planned to massacre the Jew
"wild rumors."*

Nazis always come in through the front d
They knock loudly. "Shnell!" they shout. T
means "quick" in German. Then one of them
kick the door in with his boot. Nazis always v
shiny boots.

GERMAN	ENGLISH
Achtung	Attention
Führer	Leader

6

Holocaust Tips for Kids

Deutschland	Germany
Juden	Jew
Verboten	Forbidden
Hure	Whore
Schweinhund	Swine
Frauen	Women
Kinder	Children

When Rabbi Akiva was being tortured to *ath by the Romans, his students saw him say-* *the Shema with joy, oblivious to the pain he* *s enduring. "How can you be saying Shema* *h joy," asked his students, "oblivious to the* *n you are enduring?" Rabbi Akiva said he was* *py to be able to obey God with all his life.*

There are three ways out of my house other n the front door, depending on where you are en the Nazis break in:

1. The back door, which leads to the backyard.

2. The door in the living room, which leads onto the deck.
3. The fire escape ladder beside my bedroom window.
(Note: My bedroom window faces the front of the house, so make sure all the Nazis have already gone into the house before going down the ladder or they'll see you.)

The best hiding places in my house are: at the top of the tall linen closet at the end of the hallway, inside the clothing hamper in the laundry room (try to cover yourself with the clothes), upstairs in the attic behind the summer boxes and under the green couch in the den (if you can fit).

Anne Frank hid in her attic for over two years.

Maybe I should pack more food.

You can also hide in the tree house in my backyard. I doubt the Nazis will check every tree house in America.

It will probably be difficult for them to climb trees in those boots.

Ninjas could make themselves invisible. "Absorb whatever is useful."—Bruce Lee

Maybe Kevin will let me and Deena hide in his attic.

Anna Weiss was the daughter in the movie *Holocaust*. She was sixteen, and she and her mother hid from the Nazis in a room in Inga's house. Inga was married to Karl (Anna's brother) who got sent to Buchenwald. Anyway, one night, Anna got angry at her mother for not leaving Germany when she had the chance. She yelled at her mother and ran outside. Then the Nazis raped her.

In *Enter the Dragon*, Bruce Lee's sister is about to be raped by some gangsters so she kills herself. Bruce Lee finds out that a guy named Han was behind the attack on his sister, so he kills Han and beats up Han's army.

Anna Weiss had a point.

<u>POLL TAKEN IN THE UNITED STATES, JUNE 1944:</u>
Consider the Germans a threat: *6 percent*
Consider the Japanese a threat: *9 percent*
Consider the Jews a threat: *24 percent*

These are some of the things in your house you could use as weapons: pens, pencils, scissors, a handsaw, screwdrivers, a baseball bat, a rolling pin from the kitchen, salt for throwing in Nazis' eyes, knives, forks, a hammer, toothpicks for stabbing, a blowtorch, lightbulbs for throwing, the hard end of a toothbrush, a pointy-handled comb, an ice pick, the ax, a sledgehammer, the lighter fluid from behind the barbecue that you could spray on them and then throw a match at, a shovel, the pick, a trowel, the cultivator rake, nails, screws, razor blades, sewing needles, safety pins, chisels and knitting needles.

Jews were expelled from England in 1290, France in 1306, Hungary in 1349, France again in

1394, Austria in 1421, Lithuania in 1445, Spain in 1492, Portugal in 1491 and Moravia in 1744.

Some ballpoint pens have replaceable ink cartridges. If you take the cartridge out and put a sewing needle in, you can shoot it out like a Ninja blowgun.

Rabbi Brier says that the Holocaust happened because the Jews assimilated.

That's also why Hashem made the Jews slaves in Egypt.

And why He let the Holy Temple be destroyed by the Romans.

King Solomon built the first Holy Temple. Then the Babylonians destroyed it and deported all the Jews. Seventy years later, a second temple was built. Then the Romans destroyed it and deported all the Jews.

There was no third temple.

Assimilating is when you stop being Jewish, like Woody Allen.

My mother says Woody Allen is a self-hating Jew.

The Talmud teaches that every tear that is shed by a Jew contributes in heaven to the building of the next temple.

The temple in China where they taught karate was called the Shaolin Temple. In *The Chinese Connection*, Bruce Lee plays a student who goes back to his school and finds his teacher dead. He finds out the Japanese did it and he goes to their school; he beats them all up and kills anyone who had anything to do with the killing. The best parts are when he fights a big Russian guy and also when he smashes a Japanese sign that says NO DOGS OR CHINESE ALLOWED.

My favorite Bruce Lee movie is *Game of Death*, where Bruce Lee fights Kareem Abdul-Jabbar.

Kareem Abdul-Jabbar is a Muslim.

Muslims say that Jews are the sons of dogs and pigs.

Between 1938 and 1944, over 1.5 million children under the age of sixteen were murdered by the Nazis.

HOW TO BUILD NUNCHUCKS:

1. Take an old broomstick and cut off two sixteen-inch pieces.
2. Drill a hole through each one roughly one inch down from the end.
3. Put a string through the two holes and tie the ends together.

James Caan is Jewish. He was Sonny in the movie *The Godfather.*

Art Garfunkel from Simon and Garfunkel looks a lot like Sonny, and he's also Jewish.

Mercedes and BMW used Jewish prisoners from Buchenwald to build their cars.

So did Ford.

Bayer gave chemicals to Josef Mengele to use for the experiments he was doing to the Jews. He would cut your leg open and put dirt and pieces of glass into the cut just to see what happened to you.

Jews shouldn't buy Mercedes or BMWs. Or Fords.

Sometimes, though, we buy Bayer aspirin.

Deena's parents have two Mercedes and a pool. Last year, her sister and mother both had nose jobs.

Deena also wants a nose job but her mother says not until she's sixteen.

My mother says nose jobs are for people who are ashamed to be Jewish.

If you put double-sided tape around the top of your penis and pull the skin up around it, you can tell the Nazis that you're not a Jew.

During the Inquisition, thousands of Jews

were murdered simply for refusing to convert to Christianity.

"And now," says Rabbi Brier, "you're going to violate the Shabbos?"

Houdini was also Jewish. His real name was Erich Weiss. He was an escape artist. One time they locked him in a box and put him underwater and he still managed to escape. The box was even locked from the outside.

They called him the King of Handcuffs.

To make yourself look like a Nazi, you can dye your hair blond. Your hair will still be black underneath, so you're not really assimilating.

After Kristallnacht, 30,000 Jews were put on cattle cars and sent to concentration camps. Many people suffocated before they even got there.

When they put you in a cattle car, try to get a spot near a window.

Cattle cars are locked from the outside.

Houdini's father was a rabbi. He had his own synagogue in Wisconsin.

When the cattle car comes to a stop, the Nazis will make you get out. If you are sick, they will send you to the death camps; if you are healthy, they will send you to the work camps.

You need to be in good shape for the Holocaust.

Houdini ran ten miles every day.

Bruce Lee ran six miles every day. For meals he mixed milk, eggs, meat and the blood of cows in a blender.

If you're kosher you can't have meat in your milkshake.

A famous rabbi was taken from his home by the Nazis and sent to a slave labor camp. The Nazis decided to make an example of him. In front of all the Jews, they took him outside and

rdered him to eat a piece of nonkosher meat or
ey would kill him. "I will not eat this meat" the
abbi said. The Nazis shot him in the head.

"And you," says Rabbi Brier, "you want to eat
cheeseburger."

Fifty thousand Jews were murdered in Austria.
Three hundred thousand Jews were murdered in
Romania. One hundred and forty thousand Jews
were murdered in Germany. Three million Jews
were murdered in Poland.

Kevin's family is originally from Poland.

HOW TO MAKE A BOMB FROM A TENNIS BALL:

1. Drill a hole in the tennis ball.
2. Fill the tennis ball with lots of broken-off
   match heads.
3. When you throw the ball, the match heads
   rub together and ignite, and the ball
   explodes.

Sandy Koufax was a Jew. He was a pitcher fo the Dodgers.

Q: How do you know if the firing squad is Polish
A: They're standing in a circle.

One way to survive a firing squad is to fall int the ditch just a split second before the Nazis sta shooting. Then, just wait until dark and climb ou

A lot of the people in the Holocaust movi moan and groan in the pit; if you do that they' come over and shoot you, so just be quiet and a dead.

Bruce Lee could kill a man three different way with just one blow:

1. A karate punch to the temple.
2. A karate chop to the throat.
3. An uppercut to the nose.

The ancient Egyptians said that all Jews wer lepers. Two thousand years later, so did Voltaire A hundred years later, so did Karl Marx.

Rabbi Brier said that when the Jews were fleeing Egypt, the dogs didn't bark at them and that's why dogs are rewarded with heaven.

The Nazis trained their dogs to bite the Jews.

Hitler's dog was named Blondie.

Voltaire was a founder of something called the Enlightenment.

Nazi dogs don't go to heaven.

You have surpassed all nations in impertinent fables, in bad conduct, and in barbarism. You deserve to be punished, for this is your destiny.— Voltaire

Karl Marx's father was Jewish.

Groucho Marx was Jewish. His real name was Julius Henry Marx. Chico's name was Leonard.

The Nazis did not discern between observant and nonobservant Jews. Anyone with three Jewish grandparents was considered a Jew.

19

"And you," says Rabbi Brier, "you think you can just take off your yarmulke."

Kevin calls my yarmulke a beanie. I am a Beanie Boy.

If Kevin becomes a Nazi, the first place he'll tell the SS to look for me and Deena is in his attic. But we'll be in Florida.

Anne Frank was murdered in Bergen-Belsen after someone reported the family to the Nazis, so really—don't tell anyone where you are going.

They're not really showers.

They'll probably make New York City into a ghetto, like the Warsaw Ghetto. If you live in a big city where there are Jews and one day there's a Holocaust, you should leave right away.

These are the other cities I think they'll make into ghettos: Los Angeles, Philadelphia, Chicago, Boston and San Francisco.

London, too, if they take over England.

America in German is 'Amerika.'

The rabbis showed us a movie called *Ambulance.* Some Jewish kids and their schoolteacher are forced into the back of an ambulance. The doctors lock them in, attach a hose from the exhaust pipe of the truck to the back door of the ambulance and drive away.

The world record for holding your breath is eight minutes and six seconds. Some people said Houdini could hold his breath for twelve minutes.

If you take a glass bottle, fill it with gasoline, shove a rag into the bottle and light it, you can throw it and it explodes like a bomb.

Before the Romans burned Rabbi Chananya at the stake, they wrapped his body in a Torah scroll and placed tufts of water-soaked cotton around his heart to delay his death and prolong his suffering.

Houdini's cousin was married to Moe from

The Three Stooges. Moe's real name was Moses Horowitz. He was Jewish.

So were Larry and Curly.

The Mishnah says that it was our forefather Isaac who asked God to bring suffering to the world, since suffering is a great thing. God replied that it is indeed a wonderful idea and so He made Isaac blind.

Who would want to kill the Stooges?

Sometimes the Nazis set their dogs loose on the Jews who weren't dead yet.

To stop a dog from attacking you, shove a finger up its butt.

Ninjas called that the Hidden Leaf Technique.

I heard that Billy Idol is a Nazi.

David Bowie, too.

Houdini's father was fired from his congregation for being too religious.

Cuba turned away a boat full of 1,000 Jewish refugees. So did the United States. And Turkey. Switzerland sent back 30,000.

In 1492 the Jews were expelled from Spain. The Moors turned them away, too.

At the end of the war, Hitler killed himself.

When the Americans liberated Dachau, the bodies in the ovens were still burning.

A lot of the American soldiers who freed the camps were black.

If you are black and Nazis take over, they'll make you get sterilized. That means you can't have children.

Before Hitler killed himself, he killed his dog Blondie because he didn't want her to suffer.

In a 1943 Gallup poll, 30 percent of people dismissed the news that 2 million Jews had been killed in Europe as a rumor.

Karl Brandt was a Nazi doctor. They hung him for war crimes. "It is no shame to stand on this scaffold," he said.

During the Holocaust, a Nazi doctor named Klaus Schilling infected a thousand Jews with malaria. "Please," he said at the Nuremberg trials, "let me finish my experiments."

A German officer once went to the Passover Seder of a local rabbi. The Seder service was very long, and the German officer was getting very hungry. Finally, the rabbi's wife brought out a tray full of food. The German took one bite and spat it out. "What a stupid people!" he shouted. "Waiting all this time, just to eat bitter herbs!" The German officer walked angrily out the door. "What a fool," said the rabbi. "If only he had waited a moment more, the bitter herbs would have been followed by a delicious meal."

"And that," says Rabbi Brier, "is the whole history of the Jews."

Our families will come to Miami, too, if they aven't all been murdered in the camps. Then we'll uy a big house with a tennis court and a pool and car that's not a Mercedes or a Ford, and maybe Kevin isn't a Nazi he can come visit us and we an ride bikes on the beach or something.

Seven years after the Holocaust, 400,000 Russian Jews were sent to labor camps in Siberia.

Today, *Mein Kampf* is a bestseller in the Middle East.

Graffiti in Germany: *"Six million was not enough."*

Graffiti in France: *"Death to the Jews."*

Graffiti in America: *"Israel = Nazis."*

Most of the time, Houdini had the keys.

Most of *Game of Death* where Bruce Lee fights Kareem Abdul-Jabbar wasn't really Bruce Lee. He was already dead.

Tips for hitchhiking:
1. Make a big sign.
2. Stand at the entrance to a highway.
3. Smile.
4. Stand where there's space for a car to pu
   over.
5. If you can, bring a girl along, like Deena.

Florida is 6,600 miles from Israel. We'll prob
ably go to Jerusalem and stay in the King Davi
Hotel. Deena goes there every Passover with he
family. They have a tennis court and a pool.

Smite the Heathens,
Charlie Brown

CHARLIE BROWN, WALKING DOWN the street.
He is wearing his baseball cap and is smiling.
He meets Linus.

Charlie Brown says: "There's something magi-
cal about the very first baseball game of the sea-
son."

Linus says, "Schulz died last night."

"Good grief," says Charlie Brown.

Linus and Charlie Brown, walking down the
street.

Linus says, "Last night someone spray-painted
a giant pumpkin on our front door."

Linus says, "This morning I prayed to the

Great Pumpkin to protect us from the riotin
Schulzians."

Charlie Brown asks, "How's Lucy taking it?"

Lucy strolls over.

"NEVER AGAIN!" she shouts, flipping tl
boys upside down.

Linus says, "Personally."

Charlie Brown, sitting in his beanbag chair. He
watching TV. Sally stands behind him.

Sally asks, "Are we Schulzian or Pumpkinite

Charlie Brown says, "We're Schulzian."

Charlie Brown says, "Schulzians believe in
Creator who writes and draws us every sing
day . . ."

Charlie Brown says, ". . . while Pumpkinite
like Linus and Lucy, believe in the Great Pumpk
who flies around and rewards his believers c
Halloween."

Charlie Brown says, "But ultimately, beli
should be a personal choice."

Smite the Heathens, Charlie Brown

"Which one gets more vacation?" asks Sally.
Charlie Brown rolls his eyes.

harlie Brown and Linus, standing behind the old
one wall.
Linus ducks.
Snoopy and Woodstock stroll over. Snoopy
ears a beret and carries a rifle on his shoulder.
oopy's shirt reads SCHULZ IS THE LORD.
Snoopy and Woodstock leave.
Linus stands up.
"Good grief," says Charlie Brown.

oopy sits on the roof of his doghouse, facing his
ewriter. Woodstock sits on Snoopy's shoulder.
Charlie Brown strolls over.
Snoopy hands him a page.
Charlie Brown reads: "The only final solution
to kill all the Pumpkinites as they have killed
hulz our Lord."

Charlie Brown looks up at Snoopy.

"*Mein Kampf*," says Snoopy.

Woodstock starts shouting loudly and wavi
his red pen.

"Mein editor," says Snoopy.

Snoopy sits on the roof of his doghouse, faci
his typewriter.

Snoopy types: "It was a dark and stormy nigh

Snoopy thinks.

Snoopy thinks.

Snoopy thinks.

Snoopy writes: "Because of the lousy Pun
kinites."

Snoopy smiles.

Lucy holds the football for Charlie Brown.

Lucy says, "There's so much hatred and a
mosity in this world."

Charlie Brown runs toward the football.

Smite the Heathens, Charlie Brown

Lucy says: "Maybe one day, in some distant Utopian future, we can stop this hideous cycle of violence once and for all."

Lucy pulls the ball away and Charlie Brown falls flat on his back.

"That's a beautiful sentiment," says Charlie Brown.

"I'm a beautiful person," says Lucy.

Lucy leans against Schroeder's piano as Schroeder plays.

Lucy says, "Before we get married, you should know that I don't believe in Schulz. I'm devoutly Pumpkinite."

Schroeder says, "I don't believe in either Schulz or the Great Pumpkin. I believe that our purpose on Earth is an inner journey of exploration and honesty not an outward journey of conquest and domination."

Schroeder goes back to playing his piano.

Lucy says, "I don't believe in Schulz, either."

Schroeder rolls his eyes.

Charlie Brown and Linus, standing behind the old stone wall.

Charlie Brown says, "My religion is baseball. My church is the pitcher's mound."

Charlie Brown says, "The moment a team steps onto that mystical field, all differences between them are forgotten. It is no small miracle but that, for one small moment, nine different people become as one."

Snoopy strolls over to Linus. He is carrying a baseball bat over his shoulder.

Snoopy smashes Linus in the head.

Charlie Brown says, "Good grief."

Charlie Brown, standing outside Snoopy's jail cell.

Snoopy says, "On the contrary—I plead guilty!"

Snoopy says, "I am a soldier in the army of Schulz, and I shall proudly smite the nonbeliever wherever he may be."

Charlie Brown says, "If you plead not guilty we can be home in time for dinner."

Snoopy's ears stand straight up.

Charlie Brown and Snoopy, walking home. Snoopy thinks: Even zealots get the munchies.

Lucy and Linus, walking down the street. Linus's head is wrapped in a bandage.

They meet Charlie Brown and Snoopy.

Lucy says, "We refuse to play on a baseball team with Snoopy."

Snoopy says, "I refuse to play on a baseball team with them."

Nobody says anything.

Charlie Brown says, "Hatred is something everyone can agree on."

Charlie Brown, slumped down in his beanbag chair. He is watching TV. Sally stands behind him.

Charlie Brown says, "I give up. Maybe we should all just stay apart. Maybe we should all just build our walls and fences and defend them night and day with our barbed wire and guard dogs. Why should I be the only one who cares? So what if I never see or speak to another Pumpkinite for the rest of my life? What do I care?"

Sally asks, "All the Pumpkinites?" Charlie Brown says, "All the Pumpkinites."

"Even the Little Red Haired Pumpkinites?" asks Sally.

"Aauugghh!" screams Charlie Brown.

Charlie Brown, walking across the lawn.

He meets Snoopy, who carries a rifle over his shoulder and wears a T-shirt that reads WHAT WOULD SCHULZ DO?

Behind him, a small group of Woodstocks stand in precise military formation.

Snoopy says, "Snoopy Youth."

"Good grief," says Charlie Brown.

Charlie Brown strolls over to Lucy. She is wearing a beret and a T-shirt that reads P.D.L.

They look at each other.

They look at each other.

They look at each other.

Lucy says, "Pumpkinish Defense League."

Charlie Brown rolls his eyes.

Charlie Brown, standing on the pitcher's mound. It is pouring rain.

"Good grief," says Charlie Brown.

Charlie Brown pitches and asks, "What are you called when you're not sure who the Creator is . . ."

POW! The ball is hit so hard that it flips Charlie Brown upside down.

He lands flat on his back.

". . . but you're pretty sure that He hates you?"

Linus strolls over.

"A Chucknostic," he says.

Charlie Brown, standing on the pitcher's mound. It is pouring rain.

He watches the ball as it sails over his head.

He watches the ball as it flies to the outfield.

Lucy, standing in the outfield wearing her baseball hat and her P.D.L. T-shirt. She holds a tall black flag with a large orange pumpkin on it.

"Never forget, Charlie Brown!" shouts Lucy.

The ball drops right beside her.

"Good grief," says Charlie Brown.

Snoopy, at bat. It is pouring rain.

Snoopy thinks: Everyone knows the Pumpkins

re behind Schulz's death! Pumpkins are behind
verything. Their secret international organization
overtly influences and informs every single . . .

The pitch goes whizzing past.

Snoopy swings and misses.

"Strike!" calls the umpire.

Snoopy walks angrily back to the bench.

Snoopy thinks: Sneaky Pumpkinites.

harlie Brown, standing on the pitcher's mound.
is pouring rain.

Charlie Brown pitches the ball.

There is a loud POW! as someone hits a homer
at flips Charlie Brown upside down and knocks
im out of his shoes.

Charlie Brown lands on his back atop the pitch-
's mound.

Linus approaches from second base and
chroeder approaches from home plate.

Linus says, "Can you believe those lousy
chulzians are going to beat us, Charlie Brown?"

Schroeder says, "I'll tell you what I believe. I believe in Man. I believe in feeling and music and art. I believe that we are all individual parts of one larger God, and that by serving one another we will ultimately be serving ourselves."

Schroeder walks away.

"FAG!" shouts Linus.

Snoopy, at bat. It is pouring rain.

CRACK! as he hits the ball.

Lucy runs for the ball.

Snoopy runs for the base.

Lucy runs for the ball.

Snoopy runs for the base.

CRASH! as Lucy and Snoopy violently collide.

They point at one another and shout: "NAZI!"

Charlie Brown is slumped down in his beanbag chair, watching television. Sally stands behind him.

The television announcer says, "Yesterday's collision between Snoopy and Lucy only increased tension between the rival religious sects."

Charlie Brown says, "Some people say that sports are nothing more than a tool of the government to distract us from the pain of our miserable lives."

The television announcer says, "The National Guard has been deployed as widespread rioting continues across town."

"Wanna have a catch?" asks Sally.

Charlie Brown and Sally run out the door.

Lucy sits glumly on her couch, her foot in a cast.

Snoopy lies glumly on his doghouse, his nose in a splint.

Linus sits glumly in his security blanket, his head wrapped in a bandage.

Charlie Brown stands glumly behind the old stone wall.

Nobody strolls over.

Shalom Auslander

Nobody strolls over.
Nobody strolls over.
"Good grief," says Charlie Brown.

PICADOR SHOTS

All collections are available in Picador.